CW01084954

THE ORIGINAL STORIES
PART ONE

Written by
SIMON A.C. MARTIN

With illustrations by
DEAN WALKER

Strathwood

OTHER BOOKS AVAILABLE IN
THE BRITISH RAILWAY STORIES

Tale of the Unnamed Engine
Great Western Glory

YOU CAN FIND THE ORIGINAL FILMS ON

THE BRITISH RAILWAY STORIES

Real Locations, Real Engines, Real History

This edition first published in 2022
by Strathwood Publishing Limited

ISBN 978-1-913390-35-8

Strathwood

Introduction

Author’s Foreword

In mid-2007, YouTube was not the multibillion-dollar website that it is today. It was much smaller, it owned itself, and it was home to many creative people who made films of all different varieties and styles. Knowing that I had a few stories of my own to tell, I brought together a small group of likeminded individuals to film the first few episodes of The British Railway Stories.

One small introductory trailer led to another, and another, and it was with some positive interest from fans of the genre that over the next four years 18 episodes in total were released, with over six million views recorded on a YouTube channel of just under 3000 subscribers. At the time of writing, those views now number over 12 million and we have nearly 14,000 subscribers.

The British Railway Stories had been born out of a desire to tell stories based and steeped in railway history. It was an amateur production, with a tiny budget, filmed mostly at night in hours snatched away from the day-to-day work of university and adult life.

The original stories written for YouTube were very basic and are presented within this edition with only some minor edits and corrections to bring them up to date and readable. During the lifetime of the original 18 episodes, it made a lot of people very happy, very sad, outraged, uplifted, distraught, laugh out loud and feel nostalgia for a time they had never experienced.

This is proof that my original aim of entertaining and educating were matched by inspiring others to do the same. This is a precious thing, and I will always hold onto that. For those children, and our followers, these are the stories we tell.

Simon A.C. Martin

The Original Stories

A Great Problem Goes West!

Peppercorn A1 Class Pacific, no.60114 "W.P. Allen". Allen was the first of his class in a class of 49 locomotives. None were preserved, so a new Peppercorn A1, "Tornado" was built and now runs on the main line.

This is W.P. Allen – Allen for short. He is a large, blue express engine, namely an A1 Pacific. Allen lives at Copley Hill in Leeds with many other engines, of both his class and others. He is a long, well-built blue engine, with a lipped chimney, large driving wheels and a good sense of humour. Allen is normally found pulling fast passenger trains, but sometimes pulls long goods trains to the north of the border. He is normally found in the company of a delightful old engine named Stephen (named after his designer).

Holden B12 no.8572, "Stephen". These engines were well known for their work in Anglia in the East of England. This engine has been preserved at the North Norfolk Railway.

Stephen is much older than Allen, and wiser too! He pulls local goods trains, stopping passenger trains and doesn't mind going more slowly than the other engines. He is one of the few engines that still wears the apple green of the L.N.E.R., and is proud of it, despite the paint being worn here and there.

These two engines have another shed-mate, a haughty A4 pacific, named Sir Ralph. Sir Ralph is proud of his heritage: related to the famous Gresley A3s, and a member of an elegant class of streamliners.

Gresley A4 Pacific, no.60006 "Sir Ralph Wedgwood". This elegant class of streamlined locomotives was famous for pulling many named trains, and with no.4468 "Mallard" holding the world record for speed for steam locomotives, it remains iconic to this day.

His attitude sometimes annoys the other engines, and Allen is quick to put him in his place. But he does have a big heart...somewhere in his smokebox!

This story concerns a fourth engine, not from this region. This engine was a visitor from the Western region, taking on the duties of another engine who had failed somewhere near London. This engine was very old and clanked noisily along the line. His tubes were leaking, his cylinders wheezing, yet time after time he found puff to keep going. For a whole week the old engine found himself pulling goods trains from the south to the north and would get very tired upon reaching Copley Hill: the shed and yard of Allen, Stephen, and Sir Ralph.

One day, Stephen was simmering in the yard. It had been a long day. Shunting coaches for the haughty Sir Ralph was no mean feat, and neither was preparing goods trains for the other engines. The foreman knew how hard Stephen had been working and had given him a rest. Stephen sighed. 'It's good to have some time to let your wheels rest', he said, to nobody. Just at that moment, an astronomical racket came from the junction.

There was the Western engine, wheezing into the yard, with a long line of coal trucks. 'Goodness', Stephen said, as the engine rattled past, 'he's older than me!', he said with wonderment, as the old engine kept going. There was little steam in the air, and no wonder, for the poor engine had none left to give. Wheezing badly, the engine finally stopped under the signal, on the goods line and moved no more. Stephen was concerned. 'He'll never make it back home', he said.

The "Old Western Engine", no.4137. It is very unlikely that one ventured up near Leeds in British Railways days! However, some ex-Great Western locomotives did, as we will see further into this book...

‘I only ask Allen,’ Stephen said, ‘because I’m not as sprightly as I used to be myself, and you’ve just been repaired, so, you’ll want a nice run anyway’. Allen laughed. ‘Well, if you can get the foreman to agree’, he said. ‘I’ll do it’. ‘Thank you’, Stephen said, relieved. ‘You know, we are all one railway now. I’m sure the old engine’s friends back west...’

‘Back west? Are you to say you will be helping a Western engine?’ Sir Ralph had appeared from the shed, hissing loudly.

‘Why yes, Sir Ralph’, said Allen. ‘Unless, of course, you’d do the honours?’

Sir Ralph started. ‘Honour? My good fellow’, he sniffed, ‘it is not a question of honour, but a matter of decency’. ‘Oh? And how do you figure that?’ Asked Stephen innocently.

‘Stephen, my good engine, we are Eastern region engines. It has always been like this, why, in the days of the London and North Eastern Railway, we raced the engines of the Great Western quite frequently! We were always striving to be the best, and of course, we were’.

Allen laughed. ‘The best? Maybe the clumsiest’, he said. ‘Who managed to break all the fine china on his train last week?’ Sir Ralph puffed angrily. ‘That’ he said, ‘was not my fault. If signals change at a whim while you are at speed...’ ‘Ah yes, and you’d know all about that’ said Allen, winking at Stephen.

‘Well of course! I am one of the fastest, if not the fastest engine in the land’, Sir Ralph said grandly.

'Oh good. Then you could get our Western friend here home,
safely and quickly too...'

'Heavens no', said Sir Ralph indignantly. 'I have my own trains
to pull on the morrow, thank you. I am going back into the shed,
for some oil, coal, and a good nap before my evening run'.

And with that, he disappeared back into the shed.

Allen could only laugh. 'Puffed up in the smokebox,
he is, and no mistake', he said.

'So, Stephen, where would I have to take him to?'

'Only as far as London, there'll be another engine waiting
there to take him back to his shed. Old Oak Common,
I think it says on his brake-van', Stephen said.

'Well, that'll be a good long run, to stretch my wheels. Do you
like my new chimney? They fitted it after this overhaul'.

Before Stephen could reply, the shed foreman had shouted out
something to Allen's driver.

'Ah, there's your answer Stephen', Allen said,
letting off some steam. 'I'll see you this evening when I get back'.

With that, Allen puffed out of the shed, across the points,
and towards the junction, where the old engine lay waiting for him.

Allen backs down onto the Old Western Engine's train. A "head code" indicating the type of train, has yet to be applied.

Allen backed down onto the train. ‘Right, don’t worry old timer’, Allen chortled, ‘hold on tight, keep your wheels free, and we’ll have you home in no time’.

‘Thank you’, the old engine wheezed, ‘I thought they were going to cut me up here and then!’

‘Nah’, Allen said, ‘it would have ruined the look of our junction, and besides, you’re not in that bad nick. You should see some of our tank engines, always coated in dirt and rust’.

The signal arm lifted skywards, and Allen’s driver applied his regulator.

‘We’re off! Come along’, Allen called back to the coal trucks, which muttered amongst themselves.

Starting slowly, but getting faster and faster, they pulled out of the junction, and onto the main line.

Soon, they had switched to a branch line, to allow faster traffic to pass them and were making good time.

Allen snorted in front, keeping the train moving. He felt slightly out of breath, but that was due to being stiff from the overhaul, and not the weight of the train.

They upon a station, where a worried looking V2 engine stood, waiting.

Gresley V2 no.60933 passes Allen and the Old Western Engine at speed. These magnificent locomotives are known colloquially as one of the "engines that won the war" given their prodigious feats of haulage during the Second World War.

Allen whistled as they speed past, and the V2 watched replied with a feeble 'Peeeeeeeeeeep'.

Suddenly, there was a crack, and the Western engine, dazed and confused, found himself derailed on the level crossing, and there was Allen: puffing further and further away!

'Wait!' The western engine called. 'What about me?'

Allen suddenly found that the weight of the train was lifted. Huh, he thought, the old puffer has more steam than he's letting on, so gradually got faster and faster, as he steamed through the English countryside.

Back at the level crossing, a permanent way gang had seen the derailment, and were helping to put the Western engine' back on the rails. Luckily, only his front two wheels (the pony truck) had come off, so they had little trouble.

But they had to contend with the angry cries of the road users:
the passengers of a bright red bus, the driver of a butcher's van and various incumbents of the village nearby...!

Broken couplings and automatic "continuous braking" make for a good combination of drama and disarray as Allen leaves the Old Western Engine behind at a level crossing!

Meanwhile, Allen had seen a distant signal at danger,
and began to slow down. 'Bother', he said, and we were going so well'. He stopped under the signal and was surprised to see the signalman approach them. 'Hallo,' he said.

'Hallo yourself', the signalman said sullenly, 'I haven't had any word on light engine moves'.

'We're not 'light engine',' Allen said.

'Where's your train then?' The signalmen asked.

Allen had a sudden feeling that he was going to the scrap heap. 'Um...' he grinned, nervously, 'behind us?'

The signalman merely stared at the blue engine. 'Invisible, is it?'

Allen, still smiling, remembered with a sinking feeling, the moment where it had all got too easy, a few miles back.

'I've stopped all traffic', the signalman said, 'you'd better go back and find your train!'

'Yes sir,' Allen said, and quickly backed away. At the crossing, there was a chorus of cheers as Allen, sheepishly, backed into view.

'Right. Well,' he began, but the Western engine just laughed.

'I did try to hold on tight, but my wheels weren't quite so free'.

Normally, you can't reverse back into a section of track on a working railway if you have already left that section of track. Happily, Allen did not pass the signal and was allowed to reverse back down onto the train.

This made Allen feel much better. 'Right,' he said, 'we'll get you back home as quickly...but as safely as possible', he added, remembering his taunting of Sir Ralph earlier.

He was coupled to the western engine, and with a deafening blast from his cylinders, they were off and away from the crossing.

Allen returned home early the next morning. It was still dark, and he was surprised to see Stephen waiting for him, and still shimmering.

'You needn't have waited all night for me!' Allen laughed.

'I didn't. Sir Ralph was keeping us all up last night with a lecture on why Western engines are awful!' Stephen retorted. 'I'm sticking my funnel out here to try and get some rest!'

'Ah well...you can try now', yawned Allen. 'I've had enough for a few hours'.

'Was our Western friend any hassle?' Stephen asked.

Allen smiled. 'No, no hassle at all', he said, thinking of the old engine's kind words.

The Original Stories

Veto a V2!

Gresley J50 no.68952 surveys the day's shunting of goods trains. For some years after nationalisation of the railways in 1948, the old insignia of the "Big Four" railway companies could still be seen around Great Britain.

Goods trains were the lifeblood of the L.N.E.R., coming in many forms, from the humble coal train to the elegant Royal Mail trains. Steam locomotives were generally built to do a range of work, and none quite so impressively built as the Gresley V2 locomotive: one of which had been procured for use at the yard. It was on the morning that the V2 arrived that Allen and Sir Ralph were found arguing over their duties once more.

'I absolutely REFUSE to cooperate!' Sir Ralph snorted, while Allen groaned with frustration. 'Look, I can't do both goods trains, and you've been rostered', Allen said. 'Why is it Sir Ralph, that you must be so lazy...' 'Lazy? LAZY! I am an express passenger engine,' Sir Ralph sneered, 'And so are you, lest you forget! Leave the dirty work to the dirty little tank engines and mixed traffic half-breeds, Allen!' Allen was indignant. 'Half-breeds?'

'Yes – mixed traffic engines', Sir Ralph sneered further,
'Dirty engines, don't know where they've been or what they're
built for!' Allen wheeshed angrily. 'How can you say that? Your cousins, the A3s...'

'Were passenger engines first and foremost, young Allen', Sir Ralph said sweetly. 'Besides, there's a new engine coming today, he'll be drafted in to do the goods trains, I'm sure'. Allen opened his mouth to argue further, but the foreman interrupted.

'That'll do, that'll do!' The two engines glared at one another.

'I've got better things to do than sit around arguing with you', said Sir Ralph, hissing loudly as he left the yard.

He's whinging again! Sir Ralph complains to Allen about the idea of mixed traffic locomotives.
We know that he's just being a snob...don't we?

‘Good riddance’, muttered Allen, who went off to collect his train.

Later, Stephen was resting in a siding. Having sorted all the trucks out, and the coaches, at least for a few hours, the foreman had kindly let him have a rest. But not for long. ‘Stephen, are you awake?’

Stephen opened one eye and saw the foreman. ‘Yes sir’, he said, stirring himself.

‘Good. This is Herbert, Stephen. He is a V2 engine, and the latest addition to our shed. Show him around, won’t you?’

‘Yes sir,’ said Stephen. Herbert was waiting in the shed. He looked quite nervous, and jumped when Stephen said hallo.

‘Oh! Oh, hallo’, he said, stammering slightly. ‘I’m Herbert’.

‘Stephen. Pleased to meet you’, the old engine said. ‘Have you come far?’

‘Only Doncaster. I’ve been repaired, you see. A slight accident a few weeks ago at New England’.

‘Oooh. What happened?’

‘Well, I backed into a signal box through some buffers after a bull got loose from its box’, Herbert said, looking round anxiously, as if a bovine threat might be lurking.

Stephen meets Herbert, a Gresley V2 no.60933. Herbert is a shy young locomotive, but Stephen is happy to take over the mentor role.

‘Oh dear’, Stephen said kindly, ‘well, there’s no cattle here. Why don’t you help me shunt some trucks, and I can show you about the yard?’

‘That sounds wonderful’, Herbert said, smiling for the first time.

Stephen and Herbert had a wonderful morning, although Stephen had already arranged the trucks, he had decided to keep that quiet, so that Herbert could learn the yard’s layout. Back and forth they went, until the foreman called them over, and told Stephen to take the permanent way gang up towards the tunnel.

‘While he’s doing that,’ the foreman said, ‘Herbert, you can take the next stopping train. It’s only a few carriages to take along one of the branch lines, you’ll be fine’.

‘Yes sir’, Herbert said.

Stephen took the permanent way gang in their old train, whistling to Herbert as he passed. Herbert eventually found his coaches: several old Gresley coaches that were teak in colour and started his journey. He stopped at every station, collecting passengers, and dropping them off, all afternoon. The sun shone, the rails hummed, and he felt relaxed for the first time in a while.

That evening, when he returned to the shed, he found that there was no room left, so he backed onto the coaling stage, and rested there. Everything seemed quiet...but as he started to fall asleep, he could hear muttering from the shed.

Herbert waits for the "right away" at Leeds Central station.

‘I think we should veto the V2!’ Sir Ralph said, and the other engines reacted angrily.

‘What’s he done wrong then?’ Allen asked.

‘He’s just not a proper engine,’ Sir Ralph sniffed. ‘At least the tank engines know their place and stick to it’.

There were more cries of protest, and Stephen called out for silence.

‘Sir Ralph, he seems a nice, hardworking young fellow. Why not give him a chance?’

The other engines muttered their agreement.

Sir Ralph laughed. ‘Stephen, my good chap, I’...

‘Am being very, very harsh’, Allen spoke angrily. ‘Does he not come from the same metal? Or even, dare I say it, the same works?’

Sir Ralph harrumphed.

‘Right then. Stow it in your smokebox and go to sleep’, Allen said, closing his own eyes.

Herbert felt glad that the other engines liked him but was slightly hurt. He hadn’t even met Sir Ralph yet. The next morning, Herbert ventured into the yard, and found Allen waiting, simmering.

‘Morning...you must be Herbert’ Allen yawned. ‘Welcome to the yard’.

‘Thanks’, Herbert said, slightly nervous. He was just about to move off and collect his coaches when the foreman shouted something out to Allen’s driver.

Allen started laughing. ‘I can’t go’, he said. ‘I haven’t got enough steam. Send young Herbert here, he’ll do fine’.

Herbert suddenly found himself being driven towards the main line. ‘Where are we going?’ He asked his driver.

‘Sir Ralph has failed at with hot axle boxes’, his driver replied. ‘We’re going to rescue the train’.

Herbert was thrilled!

Sir Ralph sat grumpily in a siding, while his passengers waited on the station platform.

He was most indignant when Herbert backed down onto his train. ‘They sent THAT to do my work?’ He snorted. ‘Don’t bang those coaches apart like you do to the trucks, *mixed traffic*’.

Oh dear, Sir Ralph's in trouble. Happily, Herbert is on hand to save the passengers' day!

Herbert ignored him. The signal had dropped, the guards whistle had blown, and he stormed out of the station, leaving Sir Ralph coughing in his wake of steam. That evening in the shed, Allen and Stephen were congratulating Herbert.

'A very fine piece of work', Stephen said, and Allen agreed.

'Two minutes early...even the stationmaster was impressed', Allen said.

Herbert smiled. 'Thank you', he said, 'but what has happened to Sir Ralph?' 'Oh, he's still where you left him, the works can't attend to him for a week!', Allen said, delighted.

'We're getting an engine from another region to cover for him, though', Stephen said. 'Although you pulled well enough for two today and no mistake!' Herbert was happier than he'd been in months.

Sir Ralph was cold, alone, and miserable on his siding. He'd learn his lesson, soon enough...

Steam locomotives can be temperamental beings, and none more temperamental than Sir Ralph Wedgwood, sat cold and alone in a siding...!

The Original Stories

Hawk, aye!

A Great Western design in Leeds? This was the case! Many of the 94xx locomotives were subcontracted out to locomotive works other than Swindon, so many of them were tested and then delivered from the works where they were built.

The London and North Eastern, and Great Western Railways, have always been great competitors: dating back to a time when railways were famed for their luxury, and legendary for their speed. The 1928 exchange trials had seen a Great Western triumph but arguably this spurred the L.N.E.R. into creating a certain class of high-speed steam locomotive...the Gresley A4 Pacific...

One of Copley Hill's visiting A4 Pacifics was Sir Ralph Wedgwood. Sir Ralph, as he was known, was not the original engine: rather a locomotive named in honour of another engine, a curious arrangement that no one seemed to be aware of. Sir Ralph had recently run very hot at speed and failed at a station in the central region.

After Sir Ralph had been towed to Doncaster works, Copley Hill's staff found themselves with an engine problem. While they had of course procured Herbert for the yard and had Allen and Stephen of course, there was too much work between all the engines of the yard for them to cope. Therefore, a request for a temporary addition of another engine to work at the yard was made.

The only engine available came from the Western region, recently built, and requiring running in, and so the duties of Sir Ralph were given to Herbert, Herbert's to Stephen, and the visiting engine would do Stephen's shunting for him in turn. It was perhaps ironic that the yard seemed to lose a Gresley streak and gain some Western muscle! The engine arrived two hours earlier than expected and was already shunting the trucks that same evening. 'Good morning' he said, bustling up to Allen. Allen was intrigued.

This was probably the first time since Stephen had arrived on the yard, all those years ago, that an engine had come to say 'good morning' to Allen, personally.

‘Good morning’, Allen replied, ‘What is your name?’
‘Hawksworth sir - after my designer’, he replied. ‘But everyone just calls me Hawk, sir. Shorter that way sir’.

‘That’ll do,’ Allen laughed. ‘Hawk it is then. Carry on Hawk, you’re doing a fine job with those trucks’.

‘Thank you, sir. Right away sir’. The engine said, and puffed away. Stephen and most of the yard was impressed, but Sir Ralph less so.

‘I couldn’t find my train this morning’, he complained to Herbert. ‘You always put near the coal line. The Western engine put it near the goods shed’.

‘Naturally’, Stephen said, ‘As they hadn’t put your train together yet’.

Sir Ralph Harrumphed, whilst Allen said, ‘well...fair enough. Still, he doesn’t talk much, does he?’

‘Not all engines are chatterboxes like us’, said Stephen.
‘Some engines work better if they concentrate on the job at hand, besides, he’s busy. I’m sure he’ll talk to you later when he takes a break’.

That evening, Hawk joined the other engines in the yard.

‘So, I said to my driver, there’s no way Newcastle will win the cup this year,’ Allen laughed, ‘It’ll be City’s year, I know it will...’

'Unless of course my friend, Sunderland has anything to do with it', Stephen said, and Herbert interjected 'I took a football special home once, I think Norwich took it to London, and I took it back...'

Hawk was puzzled. 'Is it football or engines?' He asked. Allen smiled. 'Both - one of the engine classes we work with sometimes were named after famous football teams'.

'Ah', said Hawk, 'Like Swindon'.

Everyone, even Stephen, burst out laughing. Hawk looked rather hurt. Allen stopped laughing and explained. 'We're not trying to insult you', he said, choosing his words carefully, 'I'm sure Swindon are a great team, but they're not really in the running for the cup...'

'Why not?' Hawk asked. 'Everyone has a shot at it'.

Stephen smiled. 'Well said! That's the spirit!'

Allen snorted, and Hawk gave him a sidelong glance.

'You know, we have a saying at Paddington' Hawk said. 'The Great Western is Right. Being Great Western...'

'No, you're not', Allen laughed, 'no more than we are L.N.E.R anymore'.

He looked to Stephen for support, but Stephen was looking thoughtful.

‘Well, we are all British Railways’, he said at last, and Allen smirked, ‘however’ (Allen stopped smirking), ‘we are what we think we are’. Allen was taken aback.

‘It says, on your tanks, and your tender, “British Railways”, doesn’t it?’

‘Well, yes’, Stephen said, ‘but I’m not talking in a tangible sense. I am an ex-L.N.E.R. engine, and I look to uphold the values it stood for, much like Hawk here. Just because something is gone physically, it doesn’t mean it has disappeared entirely’.

Allen shrugged off steam. ‘Fair enough - but I was talking about football’ he said, and Stephen laughed. Hawk kept quiet and listened to the engines reminisce about matches they’d heard about, heard, or even, in Stephen’s rare case, seen. He went to sleep, thinking about Swindon Town, and how one day, he’d like to see them play.

Every Tuesday morning, when the air is fresh and the sun barely above the horizon, a special train of vans comes from the coast to the town just outside Allen’s yard. It had been Herbert’s job, but with Sir Ralph away being fixed, he had been pulling the fast passenger trains instead. It was therefore down to Stephen to pull the goods train, along the local branch line, to the local towns and villages in the North of England.

When it arrived, early that morning, Stephen, and Allen were still asleep, while Hawk was busy arranging the yard. Hawk arranged it, and left it for Stephen to take, once it had been loaded. Of course, the goods manager had forgot that Herbert was not pulling the train, and had Hawk add extra vans onto the already heavy train.

The 94xx class of "Pannier Tanks" were the last development of a shunting type that goes back over the entire history of the Great Western Railway. Two have been preserved. They were used for shunting, goods traffic, and banking duties.

Herbert had already left with the morning's stopping train,
so, there was no chance of re-rostering the engines.

Stephen buffered up to his train. 'Goodbye Hawk,
I'll see you this evening', he called out to the Great Western
engine, and Hawk watched as he puffed away, hardly
struggling at all.

This was because the goods sidings were on a downward slope: the weight of the train was not on Stephen, just yet. Presently Stephen came to a hill, and found his wheels slipping, and his pistons gasping. 'It's never...been this bad before,' he gasped to his driver, 'This train is so heavy', and before he could do anything about it, he had stopped on the hill, panting heavily.

The guard immediately jumped out, ran back to the signal box, and telephoned for help, and Stephen's driver carefully backed them down to the bottom of the hill, and into a siding. Stephen grateful for the rest, and the drink, was worried.

Stephen backs into the siding with the heavy goods train.

‘What happens if I do that again?’ Stephen asked. ‘It won’t happen again’, said his driver. ‘We’re getting a banker this time’. They waited for another train to pass, which turned out to be Herbert’s stopping train. As he passed, he whistled loudly to them. ‘Go it Stephen’, he called out, and then, pistons snorting, Herbert was gone.

Presently, Stephen’s banker arrived, in the shape of a very worried Great Western engine! Stephen was glad to see Hawk, who explained about the mix-up. ‘It seems I let you down’, Hawk said, miserably.

Stephen laughed. ‘My old wheezing cylinders and clanking valve gear let me down, he said. ‘What say you Hawk: shall we take this hill together?’

‘Aye,’ Hawk replied, ‘but this time, together’.

Stephen whistled to Hawk, Hawk whistled to Stephen, and the heavy train began to climb the hill. Hawk pushed and puffed, and puffed and pushed, and steam bursting from his cylinders, helped Stephen over the top, and down, into the tunnel the other side.

As they puffed wearily out of the tunnel, and passed a level crossing, there was a loud whistle, a rush of wind, and Allen had rushed past them with the midday express.

Stephen and Hawk work upwards over the hill. In the age of steam, heavy goods trains would sometimes be required to be banked on hills.

That evening, in the shed, Allen heard all about it. 'Well...he did make up for his mistake', he said to Stephen. 'That takes real guts, so he can't be all bad'. Stephen smiled, but he was so tired he fell asleep. Allen suppressed a laugh and simmered.

'Is he okay?' Hawk asked, backing into the shed.

'He'll be fine', Allen said, with a smile. 'So, I heard you did well today, Great Western'. Hawk bristled, but he saw Allen laughing again. 'You're okay, Great Western' Allen said. 'So, what's Swindon like?' Hawk forgot to be cross.

'It's big, with lots of engines everywhere, you must let off steam or whistle loudly to be heard sometimes', he said, and the two engines talked into the night: One Western, One Eastern, but both assuredly, *British* Railways.

All's well that ends well. Allen makes sure Hawk knows that he did a good job at the end of a very long day on the railway!

The Original Stories

Moo-ve it along!

Tank engines come in all shapes and sizes, and do all kinds of work, but one of the most versatile tank engines that the L.N.E.R. and then British Railways, Eastern Region possessed was the Gresley designed V3 tank locomotive.

The most famous Chief Mechanical Engineer of the London and North Eastern Railway was a man better known to the world's press as Sir Nigel Gresley, but to the men of the line, his name was Herbert Nigel Gresley, C.M.E. He had designed the original A1 Pacifics, now classed A3, and had perfected his Pacific design with the graceful, yet striking A4 Pacifics, of which Sir Ralph was a proud member.

He had also designed Herbert's class, the V2s, and lots of other mixed traffic, freight, and shunting locomotives. One class of which, was the V3 tank engine. These fine engines lasted until around 1959, and sadly, none were preserved.

Sir Ralph was still at the works, and Hawk was needed back home. It seemed the engines of the yard would just have to work harder until Sir Ralph was fixed, until Copley Hill's yard manager was told of a lone V3 tank engine, that had been dumped, out of use at New England. He immediately telephoned New England yard and enquired as to its condition. When he discovered that it simply needed a crew, new paint, and some coal, he moved quickly to add the engine to the yard.

The engine's name was Nigel, and he arrived the week after Hawk had departed, cleaned, oiled, fired, and ready to work. Nigel seemed a quiet engine, and worked hard - but I suspected that it was all too easy for the powerful tank engine.

The other engines were glad of the help, but Allen and Herbert found it difficult to get anything out of him. 'He doesn't want to talk to us', Allen told Stephen one day. 'I don't understand it. I only said good morning, and he puffed away without a word!'

Herbert agreed. ‘I ca-ca-can’t understand why he ignored me, I
only said hallo’, he said, obviously hurt.

Stephen raised one eyebrow. ‘He’s probably shy!’ He said, smiling. ‘This is after all, a new yard with many strange sights and engines and of course he’ll find it hard to talk to us straight away’. Stephen puffed out of his siding, with the intention of finding Nigel to talk to.

But no matter where he went about the yard, it seemed Nigel had moved further away! In the end, Stephen gave up, and returned to the siding to have a rest. He was feeling rather glum when Nigel backed into the next siding.

‘Hallo’, the tank engine said cheerfully. ‘I’m Nigel. Nice yard, you have here, isn’t it?’

Stephen was speechless! ‘How come you kept moving away from me?’ He asked, more amused than upset. Nigel laughed.

‘I wasn’t doing it on purpose. I just wanted to finish my work
first’.

Stephen laughed. ‘Have you?’ he said, looking around the yard. He had to do a double take, as Copley Hill was completely ordered! Trucks were in their right places, coaches were organised into their rakes, and even the special train of vans was ready. ‘Silly question’, Stephen said, and smiled. ‘Well, you certainly worked very hard today. I feel I should warn you,’ he added, ‘that you may have inadvertently upset Allen and Herbert’.

A newcomer to Copley Hill!

Nigel looked surprised. 'Who?' He asked.

Stephen was puzzled. 'Why, the A1 and V2, of course', he said.

Nigel shrugged. 'Sometimes I just don't notice anyone else when I'm concentrating on my work', he said.

Stephen was sympathetic. 'Sometimes concentrating on your work is the best thing to do' he said. 'And you've probably worked at a bigger yard too, I presume?'

'Peterborough, New England shed', Nigel replied.

'Well, there you go then! You probably didn't have the time to really make friends' Stephen said, and Nigel agreed.

'It wasn't that I didn't want any - I didn't have time for any, and neither did the other engines' he said, with a wry smile. 'It must be nice to have a small yard, where everybody knows your name and number'. Stephen agreed wholeheartedly.

That evening, Herbert found himself alone with Nigel and Stephen and was surprised to hear Nigel talking to Stephen. Herbert was rather upset. He had tried to be polite earlier, but Nigel had seemingly ignored him. Herbert decided to pretend to be asleep, and listen in on the conversation further, but that plan failed badly...when he fell asleep almost instantly.

Stephen glanced over at the V2 and was surprised to see him asleep so early. 'Don't worry', he said to Nigel, who was rather bemused, 'I'm sure you'll be able to say hallo to him tomorrow'. Nigel continued to smile, with the air of one who knew more than he was letting on.

A curious bull and a frightened steam locomotive!

The next morning, a curious bull from the farm found a hole in the wall of his field. Clambering over, he found lots of grass on the overgrown track-bed and beckoned to the rest to follow. One
by one, the herd went to the bottom of their field, mooing after the bull who had made his way down the track, towards the entrance to the tunnel. The bull stopped at the gaping mouth of the tunnel and peered in.

Herbert was having a great run: the sun was shining, birds were singing, the bull was in the tunnel...the bull was in the tunnel...?!

Herbert slowed to a halt and was frozen still, petrified!

Not far from the tunnel, Nigel was simmering in the yard. He'd arranged the trucks and coaches earlier than ever, and was taking a well-earned break, when the foreman came over to see him.

'Nigel, I need you to take the cattle truck and break-van along the branch line to the tunnel' he said. 'There's a stray bull of this farmers on the line, and it's holding Herbert's train up'.

'Right', said Nigel, blowing off steam, 'I'm on my way', and with that, he puffed over the points to where the small train was waiting for him, guard, farmer, and all!

Herbert was waiting in the tunnel and refusing to come out. He had had a nasty accident with a bull once at his last yard, and since then, had been very afraid of cattle in general!!!

‘I’m not coming out’, he muttered to his driver, ‘I can’t stand cows, you know...’

The bull turned to look back at Herbert. Herbert gulped.

‘Moooo’, said the bull, mournfully. He just wanted some grass to eat. There was no grass anywhere on this strange gravel track. What was more, a strange looking brown thing was approaching him. It looked to the bull like another, larger cow, and he moved closer to it, interested.

The ‘brown cow’ was Nigel’s brake-van, and he stopped not far from the cow and the tunnel with a cattle wagon. The farmer climbed out of the brake-van, whispered sweet nothings to his prize bull, and led him into the cattle wagon, to take him back to the field. Herbert watched, mesmerised, as Nigel smiled knowingly.

Herbert started again and whistled his thanks. Nigel could only laugh as the V2 checked the level crossing for signs of cows!!!

Herbert waiting for the bull to moo-ve, whilst Nigel sits thinking it's "dairy" good work he's done!

That evening, in the shed, Herbert was telling anyone who'd listen, that Nigel had saved his life. Sir Ralph had returned and looked bored witless. He had spent a few weeks at the works while they tinkered with his wheels and motion, and this was not helping his already bad mood.

So, raising steam, and whistling loudly, he puffed away, saying 'I must go on some trial runs, you know. A few weeks in the works does make an engine stiff' as his excuse.

Herbert kept talking anyway, and Allen, still tired from his runs that day, was finding it difficult to keep it up with the ever-evolving story.

'I w-w-was surrounded by a herd of bulls, with no way through!' Herbert was telling them, 'But Nigel swooped in with his little train and scared them away! If it hadn't been for Nigel...'

Allen looked at Nigel questioningly, and Nigel simply winked back at him. Allen understood instantly and laughed.

'What an a-moo-sing tale, Herbert', Allen said. 'I feel quite moo-ved by that!' And they all laughed together in the shed!

The Original Stories

Hand of the Fair Maid

"The Fair Maid" express replaced "The Talisman" in the late 1950s on British Railways Eastern Region. This train went from London King's Cross to Perth, via Newcastle, with an engine change made on route.

The L.N.E.R. knew the power of marketing and gave the special expresses wonderful names like 'The Elizabethan', 'The Coronation', and of course, the famous 'Flying Scotsman'. When the L.N.E.R. became the Eastern region of British Railways, more named trains appeared, for the same reason: the ideals of luxury and prestige appealing to their passengers.

It was on a late summer's day, that Sir Ralph was telling a spellbound young Herbert all about the famous train.

'Yes indeed...a fine run...King's Cross, home of the greats' he said grandly. 'My cousins, the A3s, you know, started it off. First built as A1s they were rebuilt gradually over their next decade in service, and became the fastest engines in the land. Why, *Flying Scotsman* was the fastest engine in the world for a while...*Silver Link, Mallard* is the fastest of course...I wouldn't expect any of you to understand. The speeds we reached, both him and I, and my classmates, are beyond all your capabilities...'

Allen seethed with indignation. 'I could beat you any day. You're just full of hot air'.

'Hot steam, my dear Allen,' Sir Ralph smirked. 'I am a steam engine, not some trumped up gas turbine engine!'

'He IS a trumped-up engine though' Nigel whispered to Allen. 'And he is full of gas. Old Windbag!'

Allen and Nigel burst out laughing, while Sir Ralph watched indignantly. 'Perhaps you would care to make a wager Allen?' Sir Ralph said. 'We'll both pull the Mid-day express this week, and whoever makes the fastest run wins the first season of the new express, "The Fair Maid".

Sir Ralph boasts to Herbert about the speed records his class holds. The real Sir Ralph Wedgwood was of course, no slouch and that locomotive took part in trials against new steam locomotive types in the 1940s.

All the other engines held their breath. The new named express was a prestigious event in itself: it was a great challenge, with a great prize. 'Done and done!' Allen laughed. 'This'll be easy!'

'Splendid', Sir Ralph said. 'Now excuse me, I have another train to pull', and he puffed away grandly.

Allen rolled his eyes and, smiling, looked back at the other engines. They all looked slightly worried. 'Don't overdo it,' warned Nigel.

'Remember about our passengers!' Herbert said, and Stephen saved the best bit of advice until last, 'I'd pull out of it, if I were you'.

'Humph', Allen said, 'You don't think I can do it, old friend?'

Stephen looked grave. 'No Allen,' he said, 'I'm afraid I know that you can't'. Allen was taken aback. 'Why do you say that?' he asked.

Stephen sighed. 'You were built with expresses in mind, that is for sure', he said. 'But Sir Ralph and his brothers were built for speed, and speed alone. The streamlined shape isn't just for show. They serve a purpose, and that is why Sir Ralph shall win this race'.

'Humph', Allen said, sourly. 'Just you wait and see. I'll show that rotten cheese-shaped wedge what real speed is all about!' And he puffed away to find his coaches.

The two engines had agreed to be timed on their runs pulling the 'Mid-day' Fair Maid express out of London King's Cross station, as both Allen and Sir Ralph were not equipped with corridor tenders for longer runs. Further, they would only reveal the times of their runs after both had pulled their respective trains.

The other engines waited that long week for another argument to erupt, but it didn't happen: Allen was not speaking to any of the other engines, and Sir Ralph was much busier than normal, with the late-holiday goers forcing more timetabled trains.

Stephen was upset that Allen wasn't speaking to him and told Nigel so. 'We've never argued over anything before' he said, miserably. 'I'm too old for feuds, and...'

'I wouldn't worry', Nigel said, reassuringly. 'You were right, after all. Perhaps you should just cheer him on the day, encourage him anyway. Maybe he'll realise his mistake'.

Stephen smiled slightly. It was a good idea.

Sir Ralph powers over a viaduct on his way to Newcastle!

Sir Ralph had just been cleaned, his brass work shone like gold, and his whistle gleamed in the August sunrise.

'Marvellous', he said, proudly, puffing out of the yard, and working his way across to the main station.

He backed down onto his coaches. Allen was waiting at the other platform. 'Don't wait too long' Sir Ralph said sweetly. 'I'll have this train to Newcastle and back in two shakes of a shunter's pole!'

Allen simply blew off steam, smiling. Sir Ralph snorted and puffed away. Sir Ralph had a good run. No signal seemed to be against him, the passengers got in and out quickly, and soon, he could see the tall chimneys of the Newcastle factories on the skyline.

He returned to King's Cross early the next morning, and found Allen waiting, impatiently. 'Morning young Allen', Sir Ralph said. 'I hope you have a good run later out of the 'Cross'.

A Peppercorn A1 and a Gresley A4 together at London King's Cross station. This was a common sight from 1948 until the end of steam and could only be recreated as recently as 2008 with the building of no.60163 "Tornado".

‘Just you wait,’ Allen muttered, ‘I’m going to wipe the rails with you’, and with that, he puffed out of the yard and towards King’s cross Station.

Allen backed down onto the Fair Maid train, still seething. He watched the passengers boarding with angst. ‘Come on, quickly now!’ he said anxiously, his safety valves hissing noisily.

Suddenly it all seemed to happen at once. The guard blew his whistle, his driver opened his regulator, and Allen snorted out of King’s Cross station, gathering speed.

The train was heavy, but Allen refused to tire. ‘I must beat him, I must beat him,’ he panted, and began to speed up, but his driver checked him. ‘Steady on’, he said, closing the regulator, ‘we don’t want to come off the rails!’

Allen was cross, and as they approached a junction, he saw that the signal was set to ‘danger’. ‘Oh no!’ he said crossly and began to slow. But as they approached the signal, it suddenly lifted.

‘Away we go Allen’, his driver said, and Allen hastily accelerated away.

Allen roars out of the tunnel mouth at Ganwick Curve as he heads onwards towards Newcastle...

Crossing a viaduct, Allen felt the wind at his wheels and was spurred on, ever faster. It was nearly two o'clock when he could see the smog on the horizon, and presently the very same chimneys of Newcastle Sir Ralph had seen towered above him.

Allen returned to Copley Hill later that afternoon, and all the engines were there, eagerly awaiting the results. He backed down next to Sir Ralph and let off steam. 'Well, I have the results', the foreman was there, standing between the lines. 'Mr Cecil, the timekeeper, was very pleased with the two runs, however, with a time of three hours, fifty-seven minutes, the winner is Sir Ralph'.

All the engines (except Sir Ralph of course) gave a groan. 'This time is a particularly good run for an A4 pacific, with an average speed of 86 mph', the foreman continued, 'however, Mr Cecil expressed the opinion that Allen's run was more significant'.

The engines were perplexed. 'Allen made the same run in four hours and three minutes' the foreman said, 'which, while seven whole minutes slower than Sir Ralph, is five minutes quicker than any other run by other engines of his class'.

This seemed to be of little consolation to Allen. 'I still lost,' he said, downcast.

'Yes, you did,' Sir Ralph said loftily, 'however, I concede that your run was the better of the two'.

Allen was speechless! 'I was built for speed', Sir Ralph went on, '...and to come within seven minutes of me is a great feat for any engine. So, I bow to you, Allen. It was a tremendous run', and the A4 puffed grandly away.

After the race: Sir Ralph commiserates Allen at Copley Hill.

Stephen pulled up alongside Allen. ‘You did very well’ he said, smiling.

‘You were right though’ Allen said, smiling ruefully. ‘I’m...’

‘Apology accepted’, Stephen interrupted. ‘We have something more important to discuss, however’.

‘What’s that?’

‘I wish I knew. what’s got into Sir Ralph?’

All the engines agreed. Sir Ralph acting nice? What exactly had happened at the works while he’d been away?

I’m afraid for you and me, that will be another story...

But for Allen and the Fair Maid express, the story was just beginning...

The Original Stories

Goodbye, Stephen

1952. A grim year for British steam locomotives. It was the year that the British Transport Commission proposed a plan for the modernisation and re-equipment of British Railways. It was to be known as 'the Modernisation plan'.

It was to take place over a period of fifteen years, and its aim was to abolish steam traction with large scale dieselisation and large-scale electrification on the Eastern Region, Kent, Birmingham, and Central Scotland were planned.

It had only been four years since British Railways had started designing their range of 'standard' locomotives, like the Standard Class 4MT Stephen could be seen talking on a grey winter's day...

Autumn had come quickly in the year of 1952, and Stephen was talking quite gravely to one of these engines that visited often.

'I tell you Stephen, the situation's bad', the Standard Four said, looking grim, 'most of us are only a few years old, and they're still building us by the tens. The workers reckon we'll be scrapped within ten years, thanks to this plan'.

Stephen sighed. 'Have faith...there is always another plan, another scheme. They will realise their folly when the engines line up, one by one in the scrapyards, and yet the workload gets bigger and bigger...mark my words', he said, with a smile, 'It'll take more than the government's words to abolish steam completely'.

'If you say so', the Standard Four said dubiously, 'but you'll be up first then mate. You're pre - pre - grouping! If I wasn't looking at you, I'd say you were a myth - yet here you are, a ten-wheeler talking to another ten-wheeler, and there's the best part of fifty years between our designs!'

Stephen laughed. 'Age is no limit', he said, amused. 'I've come back from the brink so many times'...

'You may not come back the next time', the Standard Four warned. 'I saw a tank engine cut up on a siding the other day, where he failed'.

Stephen was shocked but tried not to show it. 'On the siding, you say?' he asked. The Standard Four looked grim. 'He burst one of his cylinders and that was that' he said. 'You could hear the screams from miles away, the torchers were brutal'.

Stephen remained quiet.

'Word is, if they think you're not worth fixing, they send you for scrap, never mind how useful you've been, or how little the damage'.

A contrast in locomotive design: fifty years spans the origins of Stephen's class and the Standard 4MT he is talking to.

You can see clearly here that Stephen has an inside cylinder layout (between the frames) whereas the Standard 4MT has his cylinders and valve gear on the outside.

The foreman shouted something to the Standard Four's driver, and he let off steam.

'Well, see you later Stephen', the engine said, 'I hope we meet again'.

'I do too', murmured Stephen, watching the Standard Four puff away.

Allen arrived back home that afternoon when the weather started to turn for the worse.

'Good grief', Allen said, 'the rain's coming. I don't envy anyone going out in this!'

'Don't envy me then', Stephen grunted, preparing to go. 'Herbert's late coming in the stopping train, I must take his goods train for him'.

Allen yawned. 'Be careful Stephen', he said. 'I know you will be, but even so I reckon some extra caution wouldn't go amiss'.

Stephen agreed and set off to find his train.

"Hector", a steam locomotive of the Royal Scot Class (as rebuilt under Sir William Stanier for the London, Midland, and Scottish Railway) is stopped awaiting a permanent way gang to finish work on a set of points.

Meanwhile, on a stretch of track past the junction, a trainload of vans had been stopped. The Midland Region Engine at the front of the train was impatient. 'I wish they'd hurry up and fix the points,' he said to his driver. 'This weather is horrible, and it hasn't even started raining yet!' His driver nodded and climbed back into the warm cab. The engine harrumphed. 'Not very talkative today, are you?' But his driver did not reply, instead talking to the fireman. 'Huh,' the engine said.

Back at the yard, and Stephen was waiting with his long train of wagons and flatbeds, for his path to clear. Finally, the signal dropped, and, puffing hard, Herbert arrived, whistling to Stephen as he passed. Stephen looked to his signal, which dropped, and the points clicked into place. 'Here we go,' he said, determinedly, and crossed over the points onto the main line.

The wind howled and Stephen, still puffing valiantly, shivered on the cold rails. He could hardly see for the cruel, cold wind, and just kept puffing along.

Back at the junction, and the points had been fixed, but there was another problem. The brakes had come hard on a few of the trucks, and the Midland engine was not happy. 'Come on', he said impatiently to his driver, 'there'll be another train in our section if we don't get a move on! We've got to keep moving!' The driver agreed, and he and the guard went along the train, checking the brakes.

Danger approaching! Look out Stephen!

Stephen was speeding up on the downward slope towards the junction, and the light was dimming, and the wind blew with him as he descended the bank. He whistled as he entered the tunnel...

The Midland engine heard the whistle, and called to his driver 'Hi, there's a train coming!' The driver looked up, past his engine, and was horrified. He scrambled into his cab, and opened the regulator feverishly, and the midland engine began to move, but the train was heavy and the rails slippery...

Stephen rounded a corner, and saw a man waving a flag madly, and then with horror saw the brake-van, too late...

...and all was silent, save for the Midland engine, pulling the remnants of his train.

Allen and Sir Ralph were resting in the shed when they heard a strange noise. It was the sound of a bell, a bell that Allen had never heard before, and it had come and gone within the space of a few minutes. 'What was that about?' Allen asked Sir Ralph, who looked grim. 'That's the emergency bell', he said. 'There's been an accident down the line somewhere...'

The foreman shouted across the yard, and Allen watched, mesmerised, as Herbert puffed up the line with a train of flat trucks, and some workers in an old carriage.

'Of course, the last time I heard that', Sir Ralph said softly, '...The year was 1942, and... well, it was one of my brothers...'

They waited up all night, to tell Stephen all about it, when he returned.

But Stephen did not come home.

That morning, that dreadful morning, Allen awoke with a start, and backing down next to him, was an engine he had never seen before. The engine, clearly of midland design, looked rather sad. 'Good morning,' the engine said politely, and Allen replied in kind.

'Do you know anything about the accident?' Allen asked, and the midland engine looked worse still.

'Know anything about it?' He said, miserably. 'It was my train that was hit from behind, by a goods train. I've spent the night clearing the wreck up with the breakdown crew, and one of your V2 engines'.

Allen couldn't understand. 'The only fast goods train was Herbert's' he said, puzzled, 'and Herbert didn't make it back in time'.

'So, I heard', the Midland engine said, 'but the foreman here re-rostered another engine to pull the train'.

Sir Ralph was wide awake now and keeping very quiet.

'All I can say is, they got the poor engine on a flatbed, and took him away sharpish', the midland engine continued sadly, 'but there wasn't much left. Look, they're bringing in his tender in now'.

Allen did not want to look, but when he did, he could think of nothing to say, think or feel. Just emptiness.

For there, between two trucks, was an old eastern tender, with faded green paint, battered, and quite alone.

'I'm so sorry', the Midland engine said to Allen, who looked away.

Sir Ralph hesitated, then carefully moved forward out of the shed. 'Don't worry', he said to the distraught Midland engine. 'It wasn't your fault. Get on home, your friends will be worried'. The Midland engine puffed away sadly.

Sir Ralph wanted to stay and talk to Allen, but his early train was due, and he puffed out of the yard, despondent.

Allen was left alone, and sad in the shed, with nothing but the sounds of the yard to comfort him.

And there, in the quiet of that yard, on a siding, stood the battered eastern tender, alone and silent.

Stephen's battered tender sits forlornly in a corner of Copley Hill's yard, whilst Allen, Sir Ralph and Hector come to terms with the night's events.

The weeks passed, and the battered tender disappeared. When exactly, no one knew, and nobody wanted to find out, for fear of something more terrible.

The yard had two new engines: one to stay permanently, the other on loan. The first was called Tavish, and he was a goods engine, of Class J39, borrowed from Scotland. He seemed rather aloof, but was an amenable chap, pulling the local goods trains.

George was brought on loan from the Midland region, and outwardly was very grumpy. But he did his work without fuss and kept Nigel company. To Nigel's delight, he was also a cricket fan, and the two tank engines grumbled into the early hours, about dropped catches, bad umpiring, and poor sportsmanship!

Allen found himself alone constantly, and did his best to stay away from the yard as much as possible. Then one day, in early October, as the weather began to change, Allen found himself back in the yard, with all the engines present.

'What's going on?' He asked Nigel. 'Why haven't you all gone to work yet?' Nigel smiled knowingly. 'The Foreman's given us five extra minutes', he said, 'he said we might want to see this'.

Meet Tavish and George!
One new resident and one new visitor to Copley Hill.

Allen was stumped. 'See what?' he asked, but as he spoke a loud, shrill whistle blew from the junction, and everyone fell silent.

Then, crossing the points, and backing towards them, from out of the morning haze, a black tender appeared, followed by a black engine, who whistled shrilly again.

Allen could not believe it. Could it be?

The engine which backed down next to him, to a chorus of cheers, and whistles, was Stephen, steaming well and polished to perfection.

'Good morning young engines', Stephen said, and beamed back at the engines.

Allen was speechless! 'I thought...we all thought', he began, but Stephen interrupted, 'It's nice to have a railway that knows the value of a decent engine' he said. 'Do you like my new mixed traffic livery?'

'My dear Stephen', Sir Ralph said, beaming. 'You look absolutely perfect! Why, I must have a wash down, and you too Allen', he said, giving Allen a rare smile, 'after all, we engines of the British Railways must stand – CLEAN – together!!!'

'Och,' Tavish murmured to Stephen, rolling his eyes, 'Perhaps ye wish ye'd maybe stayed at the works?'

Welcome home, Stephen.

The Original Stories

Christmas, 1952

Copley Hill's resident shunting engine, Gresley J50 tank locomotive no.68952 (known as Geoffrey to his friends) sits waiting for work in the frost and snow in the yard. He doesn't look very happy!

Snow came early to the British Isles, and everywhere, on every region, the engines of the British Railways found it difficult to do their work.

Unless, of course, you were Tavish the Goods engine. Tavish had been fitted with a snowplough, and, coupled up to an old carriage, spent the days clearing the tracks, come snow or shine.

The snow fell harder on Christmas eve, and Tavish found he had too much work. He'd come back from clearing one line, to find another was blocked, and it would only be a few hours until he heard of blockage elsewhere.

The goods trains were piling up in the sidings, with no sign of let-up at all. Tavish and Herbert were constantly frustrated with the sheer weight of the trains, and Herbert reckoned that he spent more time slipping on the rails than he did move!

'It's just not funny,' Herbert muttered to Stephen at the junction outside the shed. The two engines were waiting for their respective paths to clear, and Herbert was steaming. 'I only just got out of the yard this morning', he said, 'and there was more snow everywhere. Why can't the weather be good for a change?'

Scotland the Brave!
Tavish gets to work with his snowplough, clearing the main lines around Copley Hill Depot.

'Because' Stephen said, with a smile, 'this is the British Isles, the weather has always changed like this, every year, for as long as I can remember'.

Herbert blew off steam, frustrated. There was a whistle from the branch line, and Tavish appeared, dragging what appeared to be a long blue and white mound.

The "mound" turned out to be Allen, who was frozen to the tubes, and shivering as he passed them.

'Och', Tavish said grumpily, 'As if I didn't have enough work to do, ye go and get stuck in a snowbank...'

'I d-d-d-d-didn't mean t-t-t-to!' Allen shivered, and Stephen Laughed.

'It sounds like you're frozen to the tubes!'

'N-n-n-n-not quite, but I am very c-c-c-cold!' Allen said, unhappily.

Back at Copley Hill, and the engines were having something of an indignation meeting. Allen was fired up once more, and looking much happier, but Herbert, Tavish and even Nigel were cross. 'All o' this snow is taking up all my time', Tavish said. 'We need another engine to help me out'.

Frozen to the driving wheels! Tavish rescues Allen from his snowdrift escapades!

Herbert agreed, but Nigel didn't. 'If we had another engine to shunt about the yard' he said, 'the goods trains would be sorted quicker, and we wouldn't have to worry about the snow because the trains would go when the lines were clear'.

'Och, but how could the trains go when the lines aren't clear?' Tavish replied, and they only stopped arguing when Sir Ralph backed into the yard, seething with rage.

'YOU THERE! THE LITTLE GOODS ENGINE! A WORD PLEASE!'

'Whatever you've done, it's not worth arguing,' Nigel quickly advised, 'Just agree to disagree and puff away'.

'Och, I be having none o' this!' Tavish said furiously, as Sir Ralph backed down next to him.

'Why aren't you out clearing the main line?' Sir Ralph demanded, blowing off steam furiously. 'All my passengers are stuck in hotels because the line's blocked!'

‘OCH, there’s only so much one engine can do!’ Tavish responded angrily, ‘I have been working for three days solid clearing the lines, and without getting any help from any o’ you!’

‘Well naturally,’ Sir Ralph sniffed. ‘I am not a goods engine!’

‘OCH, ye couldn’t be a shunter, let alone a goods engine, ye lazy trumped up excuse fer a steam loco!’ Tavish retorted, ‘Yer just a heaping pile o’ scrap metal!’

‘Well! I...I... Never been so...OOOHHH!’ Sir Ralph hissed angrily, ‘Just you...wait.... OOOOOOOOH!’

‘Stow it you two! Achoo!’ Allen had come out of the shed, sneezing terribly. ‘Let’s concentrate on the passengers. I have an idea...’

And Allen told his driver, who told the yard’s foreman his idea. The foreman agreed and spoke to Sir Ralph’s and Tavish’s crews.

Sir Ralph and Tavish clear the lines together. Sir Ralph has never worked so hard in all his career...

Tavish snorted angrily when he heard his driver outlining the plan. 'No way – I will not work with that feeble...'

'Feeble? FEEBLE!' Sir Ralph spluttered, 'Hark at the goods snow plough thingy!'

'Thingy! Why I ought a...'

'Ah stow it!' Nigel snapped. 'It's a good idea, and we need to clear the main line'.

Grumbling fiercely, two engines puffed away.

Coupled together, back-to-back, with an old carriage between them, the two engines cleared the mainline, and each time Tavish got stuck in the snow, Sir Ralph pulled hard to free him.

It was hard, cold work, and the wind blew fiercely over the two engines, chilling them to the frames.

It was approaching midnight when their work finished, and they returned to the shed, cold and miserable.

The last train to London King's Cross emerges from the gloom, being pulled by no.E103 "Flying Scotsman".

‘Och, I don’t know why we even bothered’, Tavish grumbled to Sir Ralph. ‘It’ll just snow again soon’.

‘That’s why you cleared the snow’, Stephen said, and the engines looked to the mainline.

The signal dropped, a whistle sounded, and the last passenger train of the night puffed past the junction, and onwards, towards London King’s Cross.

Pulled by one of the Gresley Pacifics, Sir Ralph thought he recognised the locomotive, but just as soon as he had seen the number on its cab side – E103, he thought – the engine and its train had gone, leaving only steam in the darkness.

‘It wouldn’t have done to keep any passengers at the station on Christmas eve’, Stephen remarked, and the two engines looked very guilty.

‘Yes...well...’ Sir Ralph stuttered, ‘That’s...very true’.

He looked to Tavish. ‘Forgive me, Tavish. Your work is very difficult, and...’

‘Och, say no more’, Tavish said, with a wink. ‘You’ll be embarrassing yourself, otherwise’.

Sir Ralph gave a rare smile.

Allen sneezed loudly! ‘Achoo!’ He said, sniffing slightly. ‘Well, it’s just gone past midnight lads. Merry Christmas’.

‘Merry Christmas’ murmured the tired engines, who went to sleep contentedly.

Merry Christmas, from all the locomotives of Copley Hill, Leeds, 1952.

Locomotives

Background

Throughout the course of this book, the illustrations have shown a variety of locomotives and rolling stock, concentrating mostly on the presence of the steam locomotive.

All the characters have been presented in real locations, taking part in real activities the London and North Eastern Railway/British Railways would have done. Be it shunting, pulling express passenger trains, or waiting for a goods train to pass.

The characters are all based on real locomotives. Their artwork has been drawn very carefully to realistically represent the real locomotives.

Gresley Class J39

Class J39 no. 64813 waits patiently at the small fishing village of Eyemouth, in Scotland, with a mixed passenger and local goods working in June 1956.

Sir Nigel Gresley's Class J38 freight engine was initially intended to be the first L.N.E.R. Group Standard design, and a total of 35 locomotives were built and in service in the first six months of 1926. However, there were some design changes and, in the July of 1926, the first of the J39 class emerged, with larger wheels of 5ft 2in diameter.

The larger driving wheels allowed these locomotives to be used on both passenger and freight trains, although at the expense of a lower tractive effort in comparison with the J38 class. 289 of the class were built over the next fifteen years, with all but 28 of the class built at Darlington Works (the rest were built by Beyer, Peacock & Co. in 1935).

The first J39s to be built were all allocated to the North Eastern and the Southern Areas of the L.N.E.R. Later orders would include some examples built for the Scottish Area, supplementing their allocation of J38s.

Although primarily designed as a goods locomotive, the J39s with their larger diameter driving wheels did make appearances on passenger trains, especially on summer excursions during the 1930s, in a similar vein to how the Gresley J6 had been utilised.

From 1946, Thompson B1 4-6-0s took over most of their passenger services. Withdrawal of the class from service started in 1959 and was swift, with all 289 members being withdrawn from by the end of 1962.

The last member of the class, No. 64747 ("Tavish") survived at Woodford shed as a stationary boiler, until it was cut up for scrap in October 1964.

Gresley J39 Class Locomotive	
Cylinders (2)	20 in x 26 in
Motion	Stephenson
Boiler Diagram	97
Grate Area	26 sq ft
Boiler Pressure	180 psi
Driving Wheels Diameter	5 ft 2 in
Tractive Effort (at 85% cut off)	25,664 lbf
Length (over buffers)	40 ft 5.25 in
Total Weight (when full)	102 tons 1cwt
Water Capacity	3600 Gallons
Coal Capacity	5 Tons

Gresley Classes V1 & V3

Class V3 no.67652 along with no. 67647 of Class V1 await their departure from Newcastle with an enthusiasts special working during 1956.

The 2-6-2T arrangement for tank locomotives was very common in the United Kingdom, with the bulk of these operating on the Great Western Railway, and examples running with the London, Midland & Scottish Railway and then two classes for British Railways known as the Standard 2MT and 3MT classes.

On the L.N.E.R., there two classes: Sir Nigel Gresley's Class V1, which became classified V3 on rebuilding or building with a higher-pressure boiler (changing from 180 lb to 200 lb). This gave a higher tractive effort over the original design, with the intention of improving the acceleration of the locomotives on certain services.

For the purposes of identifying the original locomotives, those with the lower boiler pressure retained the V1 classification. 81 Gresley V1s were built, with 71 eventually being rebuilt to Class V3 and a batch of 10 new V3s being built instead of what would have been the final batch of V1s.

These tank locomotives incorporated Gresley's three-cylinder design with conjugated valve gear and was the first example of all three cylinders and valve chests being incorporated into a single steel casting, or "monobloc" arrangement: this was used subsequently for the prototype P2 Cock o' the North and the subsequent Gresley V2, K4 and V4 locomotive classes.

During the Second World War, the L.N.E.R. put some on loan to help with loads from the Royal Ordnance Factory at Thorp Arch in Leeds. The V1 and V3 class were built to work suburban and branch line services, duties of which they were to be found in later life on around Glasgow and Edinburgh in particular, with some kept at Hull for a similar purpose. By British Railways days, most of the class were kept in the North of England and Scotland.

The largest group of Gresley V3s outside of the north of England was at Stratford in London, with ten locomotives allocated to work Great Eastern mainline trains. These, along with a few at Norwich and King's Lynn, were moved north when Thompson L1 tank locomotives started to appear in the late 1940s. Withdrawal of the two classes started in 1960 and was swift, with the final example of class V3 being scrapped in 1964.

Gresley V3 Class Locomotive	
Cylinders (3)	16 in × 26 in
Motion	Walschaerts (conjugated to middle cylinder)
Boiler Diagram	102HP
Grate Area	22.08 sq.ft.
Boiler Pressure	200 psi
Driving Wheels Diameter	5 ft 8 in
Tractive Effort (at 85% cut off)	24,960 lbf
Length (over buffers)	32 ft 3 in
Total Weight (when full)	59 tons 2cwt
Water Capacity	2000 Gallons
Coal Capacity	4 Tons

Locomotives

Gresley V2 Class

Class V2 no. 60841 thunders through Grantham Station with a coal train, as two young boys take down its number, trainspotting, on 21st December 1962: just a few days before Christmas.

The Gresley V2 locomotives had an unusual wheel arrangement for tender locomotives in this country. They were one of only two such classes with the 2-6-2 wheel arrangement, the leading pair of wheels placed in a pony truck, and the following set in a Cartazzi arrangement, as had been standard with Gresley's other large tender engine classes. This allowed for a relatively large boiler, based on Gresley's earlier A3 class, with a wide firebox to be utilised.

Only one other class had been built as a prototype with this wheel arrangement for the Midland Railway in 1908: the Paget locomotive, which was short lived and unsuccessful.

By contrast, the Gresley V2 class was very successful, eventually numbering 184 examples and working across the mainlines of the L.N.E.R. until the end of steam on British Railways (their 22 ton axle limit prevented them from working on the more lightly laid lines, restricting them from many lines in Anglia, Scotland and the Central and North Eastern regions).

The design had been arranged as a smaller version of the Gresley A3 Pacific in many ways. The driving wheels were 6ft 2in in size, matching the Gresley P2 Mikados. This wheel diameter would eventually become the mixed traffic standard for the L.N.E.R. when Edward Thompson built the first of his ten B1 locomotives using V2 driving wheels in the 1940s.

The cylinders were arranged, as per most of Gresley's designs for the L.N.E.R., as a set of three with conjugated valve gear fitted.

Similarly to the V3 tank locomotives, the cylinders were cast in a monobloc casting when built, which was an unusual arrangement. Later in life, when the cylinder blocks became life expired, these were replaced by separately fitted cylinders. The difference externally was the addition of larger outside steam pipes into the smokebox, making them visually look even more like a scaled down version of the A3 Pacific.

By the end of steam, one of the V2s had been selected for preservation at the fledgling National Railway Museum: the class pioneer, no.4771 *Green Arrow*. This locomotive was for many years the museum's roving ambassador, with it and other locomotives returned to steam to work excursions around the country. At the time of writing, it is on loan to the new Danum Gallery, Library and Museum in Doncaster and on display in the town where it was originally built. It remains the only surviving example of the standard gauge 2-6-2 tender locomotives in the British Isles.

Gresley V2 Class Locomotive	
Cylinders (3)	18.5 in x 26 in
Motion	Walschaerts (conjugated to middle cylinder)
Boiler Diagram	109
Grate Area	41.25 sq.ft.
Boiler Pressure	220 psi
Driving Wheels Diameter	6 ft 2 in
Tractive Effort	33,730 lbf
Length (over buffers)	47 ft 2 in
Total Weight (when full)	144 Tons 2 cwt
Water Capacity	4200 Gallons
Coal Capacity	6 Tons

Locomotives

Train Spotting!

Which steam locomotives did you spot today?
Tick the box for each one you saw in the illustrations.

Class	Number	Actual/ Character Name	Wheel Arrangement	Spotted!
A1	60114	W.P.Allen / "Allen"	ooOOOo	
A3	E103	Flying Scotsman	ooOOOo	
A4	60006	Sir Ralph Wedgwood / "Sir Ralph"	ooOOOo	
B12	8572 & 61572	"Stephen"	ooOOO	
J39	64747	"Tavish"	OOO	
J50	68952	"Geoffrey"	OOO	
V2	60933	"Herbert"	oOOOo	
V3	67677	"Nigel"	oOOOo	
43xx	4317	"Old Western Engine"	oOOO	
94xx	9400	"Hawk"	OOO	
(Rebuilt) Royal Scot	46140	Hector / "The Midland Engine"	ooOOO	
Standard 4MT	75030	"Jerry"	ooOOO	
Ivatt 2MT	41242	"George"	oOOOo	

Locations

Background

These stories are based on a series of films that were produced from around 2007 for watching on YouTube. Each story has been rewritten in a minor fashion to make them more readable and relate to each other more easily.

The original YouTube films were produced by way of filming sections of a model railway, so in a sense some of the locations shown in this book are "real" insomuch that they were located entirely on a baseboard for a model railway!

The original stories were not always set in Leeds, at Copley Hill's shed and yard. That became the base of the locomotives later in the series of films.

However, Copley Hill was always present in my late grandfather's spotting notes, and his many photographs of the depot, which mostly showed Peppercorn A1s and Gresley locomotives at work.

These photographs remain in my possession and when rewriting the stories for this book, the opportunity to "ret-con" this much-loved location into the canon has been taken.

None of the locations shown in the original seven films bear much resemblance to any real locations other than the ready-to-place model railway buildings that companies such as Hornby have manufactured in the past.

Which is why our artist, Dean Walker, made great efforts in not only recreating the scenes of the stories, but in placing them into actual locations.

Terminology

Glossary

Here is a list of words, terms and railway related phrases used throughout the course of this book, and their respective definitions.

Accelerated
A word used to describe the movement of something, in this case, the speeding up of a steam locomotive.

Amalgamation
Amalgamation is the process of combining or uniting multiple entities into one form. In railway terms, this process created four large railway companies from a multitude of smaller entities in 1923 (creating the Great Western, London & North Eastern, London Midland & Scottish, and Southern Railways).

Banker & Banking Engine
A banker, or banking engine is a railway locomotive that temporarily assists a train that requires additional power or traction to climb a gradient (or bank).

British Transport Commission
The British Transport Commission (BTC) was created by the post war government of Great Britain as a part of its nationalisation scheme. This commission oversaw the operation of Britain's railways, canals, and road freight transport.

Coaling Stage
A coaling stage, coaling plant or coaling station is a facility used to load coal as fuel into steam locomotives.

Chief Mechanical Engineer

Chief Mechanical Engineer is a title that has been applied by railway companies to the person responsible for the building and maintaining of the locomotives, rolling stock and infrastructure on the railway.

Cylinder

The cylinder is the component that powers a steam locomotive, by way of steam entering the cylinder and producing reciprocal motion by way of the piston rod, to circulatory movement by of the connecting rod turning the wheels.

Headcode

Headcodes are the position of lamps on steam locomotives which show the class of train, which was important for signallers, permanent way gangs and other staff members of the working railway.

Imperial Measurements

The system of imperial units or the imperial system is the system of units first defined in the British Weights and Measures Act of 1824. This has now been largely superseded in the United Kingdom by the Metric system.

Indignation

A word used to describe anger or annoyance in response to what is perceived as unfair treatment.

Junction

A junction, in the context of ways, is a place at which two or more rail lines converge or diverge, by a physical connection (points and/or crossovers).

Level Crossing

A level crossing is where a railway line crosses a road or path at the same level as the road or path. These crossings in the steam era might have had physical gates across the railway that were operated by a Crossing Keeper. There are many different types of level crossings in the modern day, with new technologies such as CCTV and hazard detection systems being incorporated into their designs.

Light Engine

This is a term used to describe a railway locomotive that runs without drawing any carriages or wagons (on its own).

Marketing

The term marketing refers to all activities a company, service or charity does to promote and sell products or services to consumers. In railway terms, this refers to advertising in the main.

Mixed Traffic

The term "mixed traffic" is used to describe locomotives that are used for both passenger and freight trains. In practice, these locomotives do not develop as much starting tractive effort as an out and out freight locomotive but are able to haul heavier trains than a passenger locomotive.

Modernisation Plan

This was a report published in 1955 by the government of the day, intended to bring Great Britain's railways into the 20th century. The aim was to increase the speed, reliability, safety, and line capacity of the railways and encourage more passengers onto the trains and more companies to invest in freight on the railway, as a way of recovering traffic that had been lost to the roads with motorway development.

Nationalisation

This refers to the transfer of a major branch of industry or commerce from private to state ownership or control, for which the nationalization Great Britain's railways occurred in 1948 as a major example of this.

Permanent Way & Permanent Way Gang
The term "permanent way" refers to the track bed and associated infrastructure of the railway at ground level. Railway lines are divided into sections, and each section in the steam era had its own gang of men responsible supervising its condition and maintaining it, hence, "permanent way gang".

Pony Truck
Pony trucks can be seen on many larger steam locomotives, and consist of two leading, or trailing wheels set into a pivoting arrangement. These trucks are designed to steer a locomotive into corners and through complicated trackwork.

Procured
This is another way to say "obtained", usually in reference to a process which requires care or effort.

Rake (e.g. rake of coaches)
A rake is the assembly of different types of coach into a train. The number of coaches in a rake will vary.

Regulator
The regulator is the steam valve that sets a steam locomotive's speed and power. It comes in many shapes, sizes, and locations on the rear of the boiler (known as the 'back head').

Signal, Semaphore Signal, Signal Arm & Distant Signal
Signals are used on the railway to provide a way of keeping trains at set distances apart from one another. Semaphore Signals are mechanical signals which have a "signal arm" that raises or lowers to indicate whether a train can proceed. A distant signal is the first signal a driver of a train will see when approaching a signal box, usually coloured yellow.

Snowplough
A snowplough is a device mounted on a locomotive used for removing snow and ice from the railway. These can also be standalone vehicles that locomotives can push around.

Trackbed

The trackbed is the groundwork onto which a railway is laid. This is normally formed of ballast on top of embankments for drainage and support purposes.

Turntable

A turntable (in railway terms) is a device for turning locomotives and rolling stock. In the days of the steam locomotive, railways needed a way to turn the locomotives for return trips, as their controls were not designed for long periods running in reverse.

Acknowledgements

Special Thanks

I'd like to give special thanks to my immediate family: my parents Jill & Jerry, my sister Claire, my late grandmother, Monica, my Uncle Peter and Aunty Gillian. Without your help and support, The British Railway Stories wouldn't have got off the ground.

I'd like to give a million 'thank you'(s) to my incredible wife, Nada, who has encouraged me to bring the stories back to life and present them in a new format for a new generation. She is my best friend, my eternal muse, my partner for life and I don't know what I would do without her.

I'd like to pay tribute to my publisher, Kevin Derrick, for having believed in the books and supported me in picking up the pen and bringing the original stories full circle into the realm of printed media.

Finally, I'd like to give special thanks, and eternal gratitude to the man who instilled that original passion for history, railways, and a love of engineering and literature combined, in me.

To my late grandfather, Stanley Charles Carvin: who is much missed by all who knew him but will be remembered forever.